Black Girl Magic

Printed in the United States of America

First Printing, 2017

ISBN 978-0998803500

Lauren Lord
St. Petersburg, FL 33705

http://www.BlackGirlMagicBook.com
(Website Coming Soon)

This book is dedicated to my sister and illustrator, Lailah, as a reminder for her and all girls of melaninated skin to be confident in who you are because there is only ONE you; and that's your superpower- Own it to the fullest!

This is for all my black girls; the ones with the naps, kinks, curls, and swirls. When you look in the mirror, tell me what do you see? Do you see a beautiful Black girl? Because that's what I see. It starts from the inside and reflects outside of you, so first you must believe it's true.
You have Black Girl Magic, can't you see? Black Girl Magic, in you and me.

So, when you look in the mirror, tell me what do you see?
I see hues of brown glazed over your skin, skin that absorbs the Sun's rays, that's your melanin. For anyone not to Love it is probably a sin.

That's Black Girl Magic, can't you see?
Black Girl Magic, in you and me.

I see full lips the shape of a sideways heart, but when they break apart the world is showered with music full of strength, passion, and intellect.
I see Brown, Blue, Green, Hazel, or Grey eyes that exude confidence and courage to overcome any obstacle that tries to blurry your vision.

That's Black Girl Magic, can't you see?
Black Girl Magic in you and me.

I see a Smile that shines so bright despite all of society's efforts to wipe it off and see you frown I see Pride in being Black, because you are not beautiful despite your blackness; but you are MAGICALLY BEAUTIFUL because of it.

That's Black Girl Magic, can't you see?
Black Girl Magic in you and me.

I see Happiness to be a part of a culture so Rich and True, that other cultures like to appropriate it too.

That's Black Girl Magic, can't you see?
Black Girl Magic in you and me.

I see Hair that reflects your soul.
Your crown defies gravity and breaks every chain,
Symbolizing that you are unapologetically You,
Black, and like your hair; Need not be Tamed.
Black girls aren't created to fit into a certain
image or picture,
But to stand out and create their own
masterpiece.

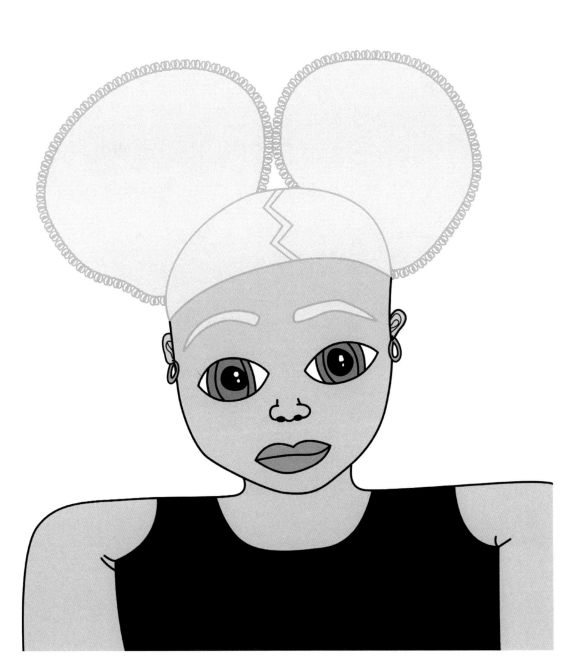

That's Black Girl Magic, can't you see?
Black Girl Magic in you and me.

I see a Black Girl that supports and uplifts other Black Girls,
Because together we, Black Girls, will change the world.

Now when you look in the mirror, if all of this is not what you see,
Then repeat after me:
I see a beautiful black princess looking at me.
I see the blessing of magical melanin all over me.
Shades of brown sugar that shimmer from the inside-out of me.

I see a bright-eyed baby doll looking at me.
I see the diversity of my family tree.
I see the endless strength that has been passed
down to me.
I see the descendent of black queens, that passed
on their royalty.

I see a wonderful person with the ability to be and do great things.
I see an awesome, intelligent, magnificent wonder looking at me.
I see the endless possibilities that lie within me, Because I can do all things through God who is the strength in me.

I see the positivity and optimism that can always
be nurtured inside me.
I see the creativity that can be awakened in me.
That's Black Girl Magic, can't you see?
Black Girl Magic in you and me.

Made in the USA
Middletown, DE
15 December 2021

55985736R00022